Cello • Book 1

Terry Shade & Jeremy Woolstenhulme

String Basics™

STEPS TO SUCCESS FOR STRING ORCHESTRA

Welcome to orchestra! We wrote this book so that we could share our ideas about learning to play cello in an orchestra. We want you to have fun and be successful as you begin your studies. Even though you will learn many things and play different kinds of music in orchestra class, practicing on your own outside the class will strengthen your playing and musical understanding. Here are some ideas to help you:

1) Choose a quiet place to practice.

2) Avoid sitting on soft surfaces like couches, or on chairs with arms that might interfere with your bowing. Use a folding chair or kitchen chair.

3) Invest in a music stand for your home so that you can see your music and play with good posture.

4) When practicing your music, focus on the hard spots to help them get easier and better.

5) Repeat the same tough spots over and over. You will improve!

6) Practice your music slowly at first, then gradually increase the tempo.

7) Always ask yourself if you are playing with good posture, holding the instrument correctly, shaping the left hand correctly, and holding the bow correctly.

8) Listen to the music you are making. Are you playing in tune? Do you like the tone you are creating?

Enjoy each new step you take as you begin to master the basics of playing the cello.

Best wishes,

Terry Shade   Jeremy Woolstenhulme

String Basics is available in SmartMusic.
To subscribe, go to www.smartmusic.com.

ISBN-10: 0-8497-3485-1 • ISBN-13: 978-0-8497-3485-4

Cello & Bow

Scroll

Pegs

Nut

Neck

Tip

Stick

Fingerboard

Upper Bout (or Shoulder)

Hair

Strings

Bridge

C Bout

Sound Post (inside)

F Hole

Lower Bout

Fine Tuner

Tailpiece

Grip

Endpin Screw

Ferrule

Endpin

Screw

Frog

Instrument and Bow Care

• Carefully handle your instrument and bow so that they are not dropped or bumped.

• Protect your instrument and bow from extreme cold, heat, and direct sunlight.

• Using a soft cloth, wipe the rosin dust off your instrument, the strings, and bow stick after you play.

• Avoid touching the bow hair with your fingers.

• Tighten the bow when you play, loosen when finished.

• Keep your instrument and bow in the case or instrument rack when they are not being played.

• Do not try to repair the instrument yourself. Talk with your teacher first.

115CO

Holding the Cello

Playing Position

• If you need it, extend an endpin strap from a chair leg or place an endpin holder on the floor about two feet in front of you.

• With your cello already placed (on its side) on the floor to your left, pick it up with both hands and lay it across your lap so that the endpin is aimed to your right.

• Loosen your endpin screw and pull out the endpin to the length designated by your teacher. Tighten the screw.

• Put your cello in front of you and stand up. Position your feet in front of the chair legs and place the point of the endpin about 2 feet in front of you, forming a triangle with both feet.

• Sit down on the edge of your chair and bring the cello into your body. It should be centered right in the middle of your body with the neck on your left side.

• Check to see that the C-peg is behind your left ear and that you have approximately two inches between your shoulder and the cello's neck.

• With your right thumb and first finger, make a backwards "L."

• Rest your thumb on the side of the fingerboard (about 3–4 inches from the end of the fingerboard).

A Brief History

Kevin Lee, a luthier, in his workshop

Travel back in time to Cremona, Italy, during the mid-to-late-1500s, and you will find a thriving town. In the middle of the musical activities is the Amati family, famous for building the first modern violin. String music was just then becoming popular among the nobility and street musicians, and the number of string instruments being built was quickly increasing. Other master violinmakers in Italy included Stradivari, Guarneri, and Guadagnini. Workshops in France, Germany, and Czechoslovakia also began to emerge. Today, string instrument makers, called luthiers, can be found around the world.

Cellos are made of specially seasoned/aged woods, particularly spruce and maple. You'll find at least 70 parts make up one instrument! Chisels, scrapers, and gouges are just some of the tools required to make an instrument. Glue and varnish are also important when making a string instrument.

Although the strings and small parts of string instruments must be replaced from time to time, most violins, violas, cellos, and basses can last forever, especially if they are well cared for. Many of the better quality instruments improve over time.

4 # Reading Music & Establishing Group Pulse

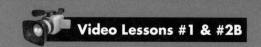

Steps to Success:
- ❏ Play quarter notes and quarter rests
- ❏ Play open D and A with pizzicato
- ❏ Establish group pulse
- ❏ Understand symbols on the staff

Pluck Open D and A

D   A

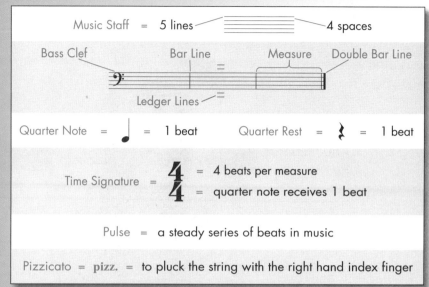

Music Staff	=	5 lines / 4 spaces
Bass Clef		Bar Line Measure Double Bar Line
		Ledger Lines
Quarter Note	= ♩ =	1 beat
Quarter Rest	= 𝄽 =	1 beat
Time Signature	= **4/4**	= 4 beats per measure = quarter note receives 1 beat
Pulse	=	a steady series of beats in music
Pizzicato = **pizz.**	=	to pluck the string with the right hand index finger

To enhance practicing, use the recorded accompaniments, video lessons, and more provided in the **String Basics Interactive Practice Studio**. See the Inside Front Cover for more information.

1. Open D and Quarter Rests

"Rest 2 3 4"

"D   D   D   D   Rest Rest Rest Rest   D   D   D   D   Rest Rest Rest Rest"

2. Open A and Quarter Rests

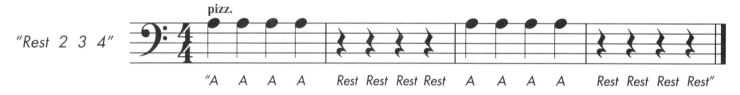

"Rest 2 3 4"

"A   A   A   A   Rest Rest Rest Rest   A   A   A   A   Rest Rest Rest Rest"

3. D and A are Dazzling!

4. String to String

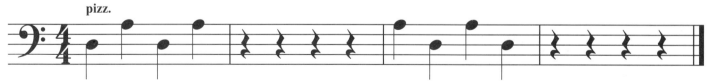

5. Pizzicato Passage

Video Lesson #3

Steps to Success:
- ❏ Play half notes and half rests
- ❏ Play open D and A with pizzicato
- ❏ Strengthen group pulse

Half Note = 𝅗𝅥 = 𝅘𝅥 + 𝅘𝅥 = 2 beats

Half Rest = ▬ = 𝄽 + 𝄽 = 2 beats

Sing and say half notes:

"D   2   D   4"

Count rests aloud:

"Rest Rest Rest Rest"

Play pizzicato

6. Hello Half Note

"Rest 2 3 4"

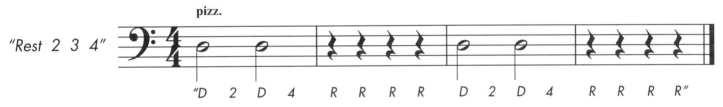

"D   2   D   4   R   R   R   R   D   2   D   4   R   R   R   R"

7. Half Note and Half Rest

"R   R"

8. "A" Is It

"A   2   A   4   R   R   R   R"

9. Play and Rest

10. Halves are Great

Steps to Success:
- ❏ Play rhythm combinations
- ❏ Understand repeat sign
- ❏ Strengthen group pulse
- ❏ Draw clefs and notes on the staff

Repeat Sign = ⁝ = go back and play again

11. Combo Time

"Rest 2 3 4"

12. Think Quickly   *Test Line*

13. Play It Twice

Repeat

"D   2   D   D"

14. Opposites Attract

Repeat

"D   D   D   4"

15. Two for Two

16. We Count Together

17. Steps to Learning Theory

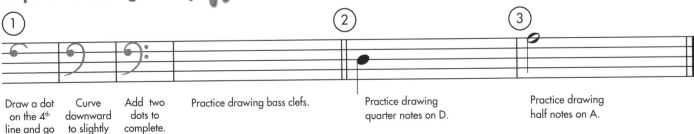

Draw a dot on the 4th line and go upward to top line.

Curve downward to slightly below the 2nd line.

Add two dots to complete.

Practice drawing bass clefs.

Practice drawing quarter notes on D.

Practice drawing half notes on A.

115CO

Whole Note & Whole Rest

Steps to Success:
❏ Play whole notes and whole rests
❏ Understand trio and duet

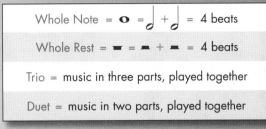

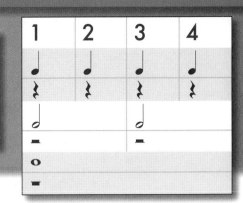

18. Totally Whole Notes

"D 2 3 4"

19. Three-Way Pizzicato – *Trio*

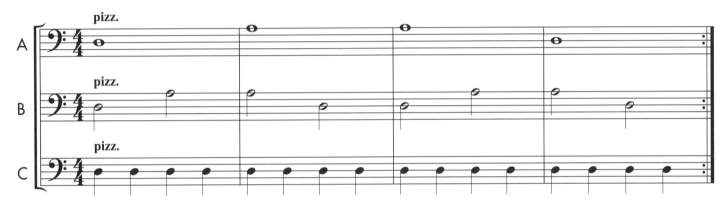

20. Quarter/Whole Jazz

21. Pulse Is a Must – *Duet*

22. Crazy Counting — *TEST LINE*

115CO

8 D String Note: 1ˢᵗ Finger E

Steps to Success:

❑ Place 1ˢᵗ finger on note E

❑ Play with good left hand shape

❑ Draw notes on the staff

❑ Create 4 measures to compose a song

E: 1ˢᵗ finger on D string

Placing Finger on the String

• Make a circle as if holding a soda can

• Keep thumb slightly bent and placed under the neck

• Place thumb directly under 2ⁿᵈ finger

• Press 1ˢᵗ finger on the D string on the 1ˢᵗ finger tape

• Hover other fingers over the D string

23. First Finger E!

"D 2 D 4   R R R R   E 2 E 4   R R R R   D 2 D 4   R R R R   E 2 E 4   R R R R"

24. E for Excellence

25. Easy E

26. One Digit Essay

27. D, E, A Debut

28. Steps to Learning Composition

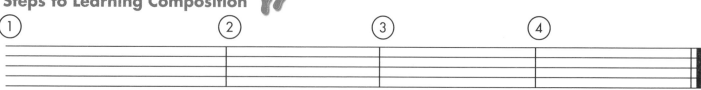

① Write in your clef. Add the time signature. Write 1 whole note on D.

② Choose 2 notes that add up to 4 beats. Write these notes on E.

③ Write 4 quarter notes on pitches using D, E, and A.

④ Create your own measure using a combination of half notes and quarter notes. Write these notes on D and A. Play your song.

Steps to Success:

❏ Place 3rd finger on note F#
❏ Place 4th finger on note G
❏ Play with good left hand shape

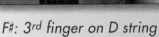

F#: 3rd finger on D string

G: 4th finger on D string

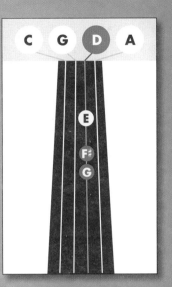

29. Clouds of Many Colors

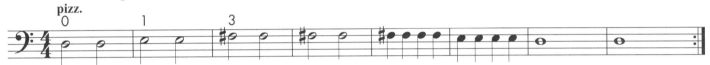

Remember to sing and play.

30. F-Sharp Fiddlin'

31. Merrily We Roll Along

Traditional

32. Platform Shoes – *Duet*

33. Steak and Kidney Pie

TEST LINE

English Folk Song

34. Jingle Bells

J. S. Pierpont (1822–1893)
American Composer

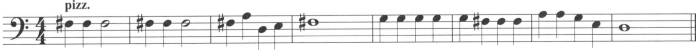

D String Notes, Continued

Steps to Success:
- ❏ Play D, E, F♯, G, and A with group pulse
- ❏ Keep LH fingers down on G when playing open A
- ❏ Understand Solo and Tutti

Solo	=	Music played by one player
Tutti	=	Everyone plays together

35. Five-Note Delight – *New Step for Bass*

36. Plaza de Armas

37. Up and Down

38. Countryside Sunrise – *Duet*

39. Skip and Step

40. Sans Souci

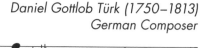

Daniel Gottlob Türk (1750–1813)
German Composer

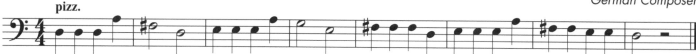

41. Good King Wenceslas

English Carol

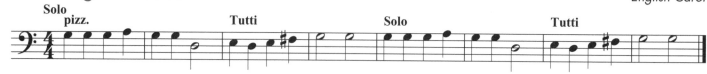

Steps to Success:
- Place 1st finger on note B
- Sight read notes and rhythms accurately
- Name notes on the staff

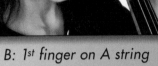
B: 1st finger on A string

42. Six-Note Delight

"Rest 2 3 4"

43. Note-Rest Antics

Remember to say rests aloud.

44. Beginning to See B – *Duet*

45. Old MacDonald – *Sight Reading Line*

American Folk Song

46. Cowboy Trail

47. The Escalator – *Steps to Learning Theory*

Write the letter name below each note.

A String Note: 3rd Finger C#

Steps to Success:
- ❑ Place 3rd finger on note C#
- ❑ Play with good left hand shape and overall posture
- ❑ Understand Common Time

Time Signature
Common Time $= \mathbf{C} = \frac{4}{4}$

C#: 3rd finger on A string

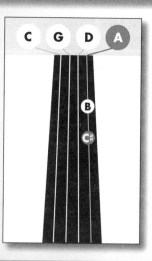

48. A String – *Add Low B and C# for Bass*

49. French Café – *Duet*

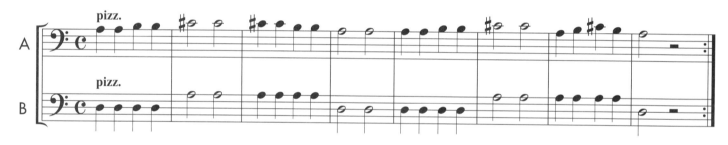

50. Hot Cross Buns

English Folk Song

51. Das Wiegenlied

German Folk Song

52. 7th Street Stroll   TEST LINE

115CO

Key of D Major

Steps to Success:

❏ Understand D Major key signature

❏ Play **D Major Scale** from memory

❏ Write the D Major Scale

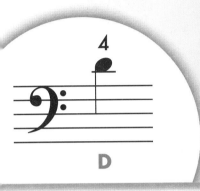

Key Signature (D Major) =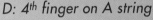

= sharps at the beginning of the staff showing what notes are always sharp. In D Major, play all F's as F♯ and all C's as C♯.

Scale = a series of notes placed in stepwise ascending or descending order. #53 is a D Major Scale.

D: 4th finger on A string

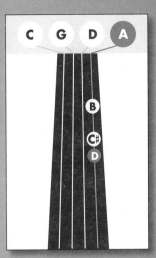

---

53. D Major Scale

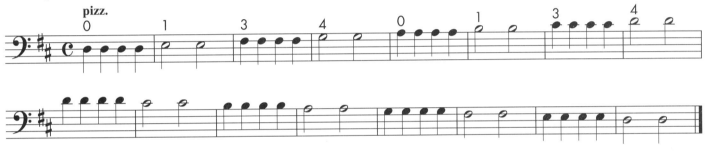

54. Country Gardens

English Folk Song

55. Autumn Breeze

56. Bamboo Flute

Chinese Folk Song

57. D Major Scale – *Steps to Learning Theory – Memorization Line*

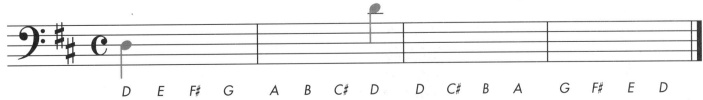

Using quarter notes, draw each note on the staff. To help you draw the notes and stems correctly, look at the other notes on this page and try to match them.

Video Lessons #5, #7

Steps to Success:

❏ Form pre-bow hold at balance point
❏ Play with smooth bow strokes on D and A
❏ Play half notes/rests and quarter notes/rests
❏ Play arco, down bow, and up bow

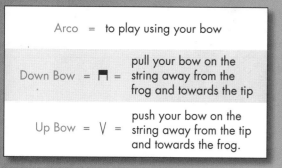

Basic hand shape

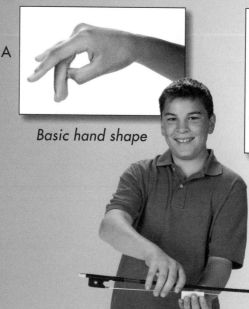

Find the balance point of your bow using middle fingers and thumb

Pre-Bow hold on rosin. The rosin remains still as the bow moves back and forth.

Arco	=		to play using your bow
Down Bow	=	⊓ =	pull your bow on the string away from the frog and towards the tip
Up Bow	=	V =	push your bow on the string away from the tip and towards the frog.

Rosin Bowing

58. Thumb to Tip/Tip to Thumb

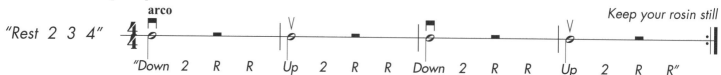

"Rest 2 3 4"   "Down 2 R R Up 2 R R Down 2 R R Up 2 R R"   *Keep your rosin still*

59. Rosin Half Notes

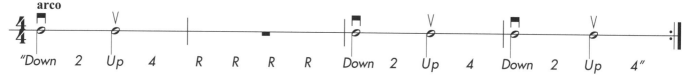

"Down 2 Up 4 R R R R Down 2 Up 4 Down 2 Up 4"

60. Rosin Dust

Bowing Open Strings

61. Slow Bow, Here We Go!

62. Slow and Smooth

63. Arco A

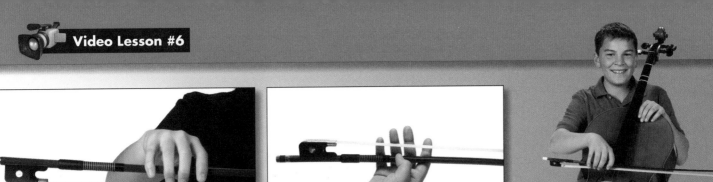

Video Lesson #6

Add other fingers with pinky wrapped over the stick

Upside down view with emphasis on thumb shape

Pre-Bow hold on strings

Rosin Bowing

64. Quarter Note Contact

Keep your rosin still

"Rest 2 3 4"

65. Thumb to Tip – Faster Now

66. Rosin Wild

Freeze *Freeze*

Bowing Open String Quarter Notes

67. Pull & Push

68. Bowing Straight on A

Use thumb to tip bowing.

69. Quarters Together

Freeze *Freeze*

Steps to Success:

- ❏ Hold bow correctly in pre-bow hold position
- ❏ Play bow lift (lift and set)
- ❏ Bow half and quarter notes using different bow speeds

Bow Lift = ❜ = lift the bow and set it back towards the frog

Bow lift

Rest position

Rosin Bowing

70. Slow-Fast Bow Speed

Keep your rosin still

71. Lift and Set

Lift and set

Lift and set

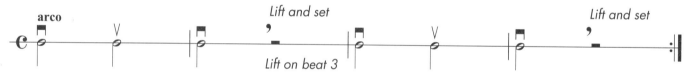

Lift on beat 3

72. Change Is Good

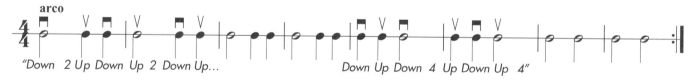

"Down 2 Up Down Up 2 Down Up...

Down Up Down 4 Up Down Up 4"

Bowing Open String Combinations

73. Arco Avenue

74. Bow Lift Boulevard

Lift and set

Lift and set

75. Combo Causeway

TEST LINE

115CO

Arco on Three Open Strings

Steps to Success:
❏ Play whole notes with the bow
❏ Play **Three-Speed Mastery** from memory
❏ Play open G with the bow
❏ Sight read notes and rhythms accurately
❏ Draw bar lines in 4/4

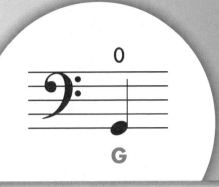

76. How Slow Can You Go?

77. Three-Speed Mastery – *Memorization Line*

78. Go-G-Go!

79. Grand G Tango

80. Waves – *Sight Reading Line*

Look ahead as you prepare to cross strings.

81. Bow Speed Is Key – *Steps to Learning Theory*

Say the counting to help you draw in the bar lines.

Steps to Success:
- Form bow hold at the frog
- Play D, E, F#, and G with the bow
- Bow whole, half, and quarter notes using different bow speeds

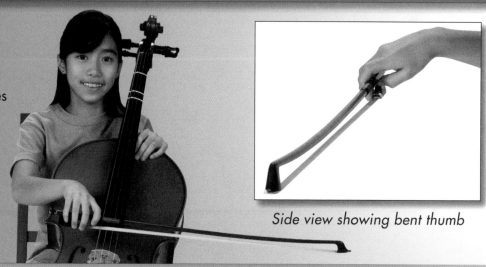

Pinky wrapped over the stick

Side view showing bent thumb

82. D & E If You Please

83. Hill Country Memories

84. Cathedral Rock

85. Warehouse Warm-Up

86. A Tune for Us

87. At Pierrot's Door – *Duet*

French Folk Song

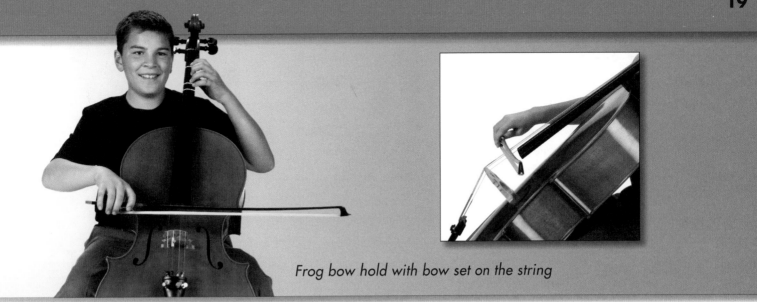

Frog bow hold with bow set on the string

88. Western Skies – *Duet*

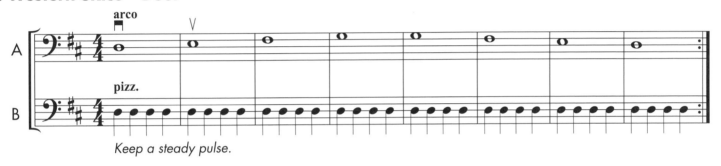

Keep a steady pulse.

89. Bile 'em Cabbage Down

American Fiddle Tune

90. Quarter Note Fever – *Duet*

91. The Old Grey Goose

Traditional

92. Fiddler's Dream — TEST LINE

115CO

Steps to Success:

❏ Play with smooth string crossings to/from the D and A strings

❏ Order 4 measures to compose a song

Bow on the A string

Bow on the D string

93. Up to B

94. Jambalaya

95. Sauntering on Saturday

96. Cross With Care

Quick lift

97. London Bridge

Traditional

98. Acadian Lullaby   *TEST LINE*

Nova Scotian Folk Song

99. Steps to Learning Composition

Title_____   Composer_____

1) Draw your clef, key signature, and the $\frac{4}{4}$ time signature.
2) Rewrite the measures provided in a different order to compose your own song.
3) Add a title and write your name as the composer. Play your new song.

Intervals, Rounds / Bass: Shifting to C# and D

 **Video Lesson #9**

Steps to Success:

☐ Understand intervals

☐ Understand rounds

Interval =	the distance between two notes. See #101 for commonly found intervals.
Round =	music where two or more players play the same melody but begin at different times.

100. D Major Scale – *New Step for Bass*

101. D Major Interval Etude

└ 2nd ┘ └ 3rd ┘ └ 4th ┘ └ 5th ┘ └ 6th ┘ └ 7th ┘ └ octave ┘

102. Shifty Basses

Slow bow speed

103. Scotland's Burning – *Round*

Traditional

Keep fingers down

104. Keep on Shifting

Stop at the tip

Steps to Success:
❏ Identify and create intervals

105. 4th Finger Duet – *New Step for Violin & Viola*

106. Tuning 4th Finger – *Duet*

107. Theme From Symphony No. 9: "Ode to Joy"

Ludwig van Beethoven (1770–1827)
German Composer

108. Obwisana

Ghanaian Folk Song

109. Steps to Learning Theory

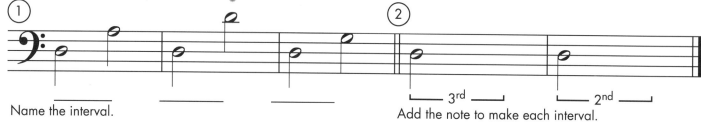

Name the interval.

Add the note to make each interval.

Steps to Success:
❏ Play in D Major
❏ Sight read accurately

110. Fox and Goose – *Sight Reading Line*

German Folk Song

111. Canon in D – *Round*

Johann Pachelbel (1653–1706)
German Composer

112. Brandenburg Reflections

Johann Sebastian Bach (1685–1750)
German Composer

113. Ophelia's Song

Deborah Gilmour Smyth (b. 1956)
American Composer

Video Demonstration

Student Narrator #1: My name is _____, and I play the _____. The first skills we learn in orchestra are to hold our instruments properly and to pluck the open strings. We would like to demonstrate pizzicato for you using quarter notes, half notes, and whole notes. Notice how we can sing and play at the same time!

114. Plucking Open Strings

Student Narrator #2: My name is _____, and I play the _____. As we become more advanced, we press our left hand fingers down on the strings. Let us demonstrate this by performing a song made famous by Wolfgang Amadeus Mozart. First, we will play the melody together. The second time through, we will add a harmony part.

115. Plucking "Twinkle, Twinkle" – *Duet*

Traditional

Student Narrator #3: My name is _____, and I play the _____. The next step is to learn to hold the bow correctly. Our goal is to draw the bow perfectly straight across the string. Watch how all of our bows travel in the same direction and at the same speed.

116. Bowing Open Strings

Student Narrator #4: My name is _____, and I play the _____. Putting all of these skills together has finally arrived. Practicing scales every day helps us learn how to play in tune as a group. We would like to play for you our special arrangement of the "D Major Scale."

117. D Major Scale – *Orchestra Arrangement*

Student Narrator #5: My name is _____, and I play the _____. Learning to count together, bow together, and play songs together is wonderful. We would like to play a folk song for you called "Lightly Row."

118. Lightly Row – *Duet*

Traditional

Student Narrator #6: My name is _____, and I play the _____. In closing, "Orchestra March" is our first piece with four-part harmony. We hope you enjoy it!

119. Orchestra March – *Orchestra Arrangement*

Jeremy Woolstenhulme (b. 1974)
American Composer

115CO

Steps to Success:

❑ Play G, A, B, C on the G string with group pulse

❑ Understand G Major key signature

❑ Name notes on the staff

G Major =  = 1 sharp. Play all F's as F♯.

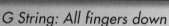

G String: All fingers down

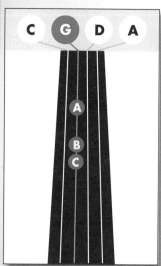

120. G to C

121. Gems on G

122. Jazzy G – *Duet*

123. Steps in G – *Steps to Learning Theory*

Write the letter name below each note.

124. Theme From Symphony No. 9

Antonín Dvořák (1841–1904)
Czech Composer

G Major Scale

Steps to Success:
- ❏ Play **G Major Scale** from memory
- ❏ Recognize and name intervals

125. G Major Scale – *Memorization Line*

126. G Major Etude – *Steps to Learning Theory*

Name the interval. ____ ____ ____ ____ ____

127. Das Steckenpferd   TEST LINE   *German Folk Song*

128. Duérmete, Mi Niño   *Argentinian Folk Song*

129. Reuben & Rachel   *Traditional*

130. Jolly Old St. Nicholas   *Traditional*

Steps to Success:
- ❏ Play 2-note slurs on one string
- ❏ Play 2-note slurs crossing strings
- ❏ Play **Slurring the Scale** from memory

> Slur = a curved line connecting 2 or more different pitches in a single bow stroke. Slurred notes are played smoothly.

131. Slur Melody

When slurring, keep your bow moving as you change pitches.

132. Searching for Slurs

133. Morning on the Potomac

134. Slurring the Scale – *Memorization Line*

135. Cross Strings Countdown

136. Smooth Sailing

137. Slurs for Sure

Ties

Steps to Success:
- ❏ Play tied notes

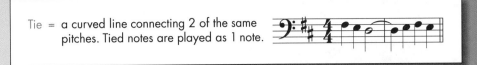
Tie = a curved line connecting 2 of the same pitches. Tied notes are played as 1 note.

138. Ties Add Notes Together

"D   4   1"

139. More Connections

Thomas Haynes Bayly (1797–1839)
British Composer

140. Long, Long Ago

141. Hungarian Dance No. 5
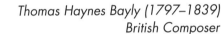
TEST LINE

Johannes Brahms (1833–1897)
German Composer

142. Theme From "London" Symphony
Franz Josef Haydn (1732–1809)
German Composer

143. The Dreidel Song
Jewish Folk Song

Keep F# down

Play smoothly and connected.

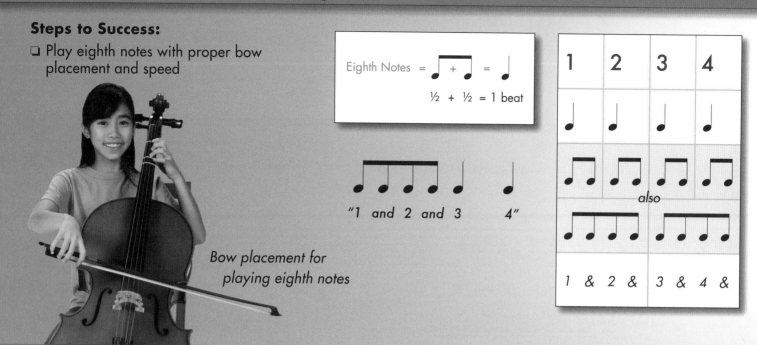

Steps to Success:
- ❑ Play eighth notes with proper bow placement and speed

Bow placement for playing eighth notes

144. Groups of Four

145. Reverse Rhythm Recreation

146. Bow Division Expedition

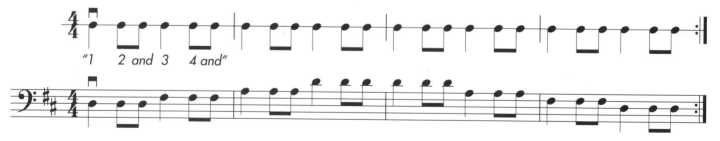

147. Four By Eight

$\frac{2}{4}$ Time Signature

Steps to Success:
- ❏ Understand $\frac{2}{4}$ time
- ❏ Understand quartet
- ❏ Draw bar lines in $\frac{2}{4}$

Time Signature =	$\frac{2}{4}$	= 2 beats per measure
		= quarter note receives 1 beat

Quartet = music in four parts, played together

148. Combo Quartet

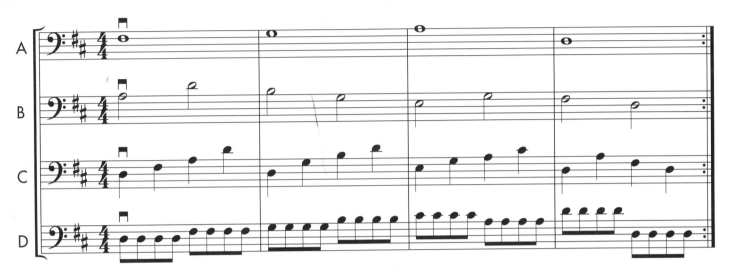

149. Frère Jacques – *Round*

French Folk Song

150. Can-Can, If You Can Can

Jacques Offenbach (1819–1880)
French Composer

151. Loch Lomond

Scottish Folk Song

152. Trumpet Tune – *Steps to Learning Theory*

Cornelius Gurlitt (1820–1901)
German Composer

Say the counting to help you draw in the bar lines.

Steps to Success:

❏ Place 2nd finger on note F

❏ Play with good left hand shape

Natural = ♮ = cancels a sharp

F-Natural

F♮: 2nd finger on the D string

153. F-Natural Frontier – *Duet*

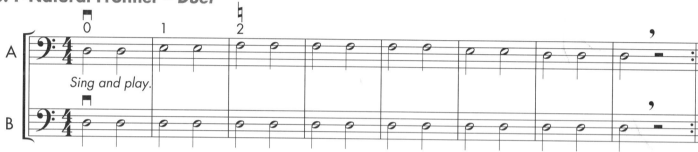

Sing and play.

154. The DJ's Rock Sensation

155. Reach for G – *Duet*

156. Theme From Symphony No. 1

Gustav Mahler (1860–1911)
Austrian Composer

157. The *Muir* Woods Trail   **TEST LINE**

Steps to Success:

☐ Place 2nd finger on note C

☐ Understand pick-up notes

☐ Understand fermata

Pick-Up Note = one or more notes coming before the first full measure of music

Fermata = play the note longer than its value

C♮: 2nd finger on the A string

C-Natural

158. C-Natural Cityscape

159. Adding D – *New Steps for Bass*

160. Sad Scale

161. Shalom, Chaverim

Israeli Folk Song

162. Bourrée

Johann Sebastian Bach (1685–1750)
German Composer

163. Snake Charmer

Traditional

 **Video Lesson #12**

Steps to Success:

❏ Understand 1-2 and 1-3 finger patterns
❏ Recognize finger patterns in the music
❏ Identify F#s and C♮s
❏ Sight read accurately in G Major using mixed finger patterns

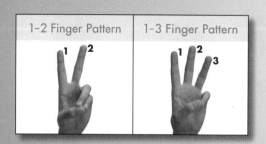

Using 2nd and 3rd finger within a piece of music

• 1st finger serves as an anchor finger
• left hand fingers remain rounded and notes are played with the tips of fingers

164. A Change of Pattern

165. Old Joe Clark – *Steps to Learning Theory*

American Folk Song

Write in the correct finger number, 2 or 3.   Write in the correct finger number, 2 or 3.

166. Mix and Match – *Steps to Learning Theory*

Circle every F# and C♮.

167. Mixed Pattern Blues

168. Theme From "Surprise" Symphony – *Sight Reading Line*

Franz Josef Haydn (1732–1809)
German Composer

Pluck holding the bow in your hand.

169. Mysterious Forest

Steps to Success:

❏ Understand C Major key signature
❏ Play in C Major with mixed finger patterns
❏ Understand 1st & 2nd endings
❏ Write finger patterns on G, D, and A strings

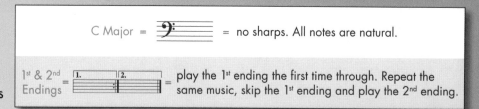

C Major = 𝄢 = no sharps. All notes are natural.

1st & 2nd Endings = play the 1st ending the first time through. Repeat the same music, skip the 1st ending and play the 2nd ending.

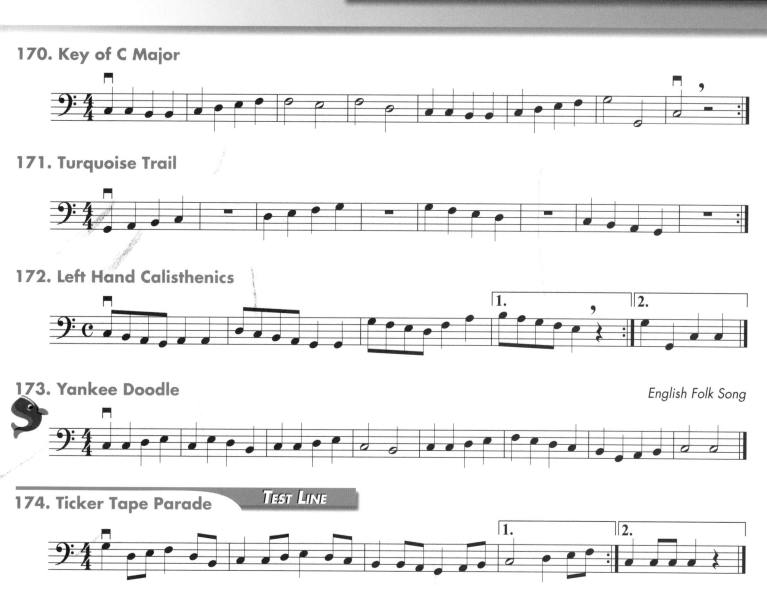

170. Key of C Major

171. Turquoise Trail

172. Left Hand Calisthenics

173. Yankee Doodle

English Folk Song

174. Ticker Tape Parade

TEST LINE

175. Theme From Symphony No. 1

Johannes Brahms (1833–1897)
German Composer

176. Steps to Learning Theory

You now know how to use 2nd and 3rd fingers. For each key signature below, write in the correct finger number (your answer will be 2 or 3).

D Major ♯♯	**G Major** ♯	**C Major** (No Sharps)
(No D Major on G String, yet.)	G String _____	G String _____
D String _____	D String _____	D String _____
A String _____	A String _____	A String _____

115CO

$\frac{3}{4}$ Time Signature & Dotted Half Notes

Steps to Success:
- ❑ Play dotted half notes
- ❑ Play in $\frac{3}{4}$ with group pulse
- ❑ Sight read notes and rhythms accurately in $\frac{3}{4}$
- ❑ Draw bar lines in $\frac{3}{4}$
- ❑ Conduct $\frac{3}{4}$ pattern

| Time Signature = | $\mathbf{3}$ | = 3 beats per measure |
| | $\mathbf{4}$ | = type of note receiving 1 beat |

Dotted Half Note = ♩. = 3 beats — the dot adds half the value of the note — $\frac{♩}{2} + \frac{.}{1}$ = 3 beats

Conducting Pattern = = A 3-beat pattern

177. Conducting in Three

"D 2 3"

178. D Major in Three

179. $\frac{3}{4}$ Climb – *Sight Reading Line*

180. Vals Bonito – *Steps to Learning Theory*

Say the counting to help you draw in the bar lines.

181. Postcards from Loire Valley

French Folk Song

182. Roses from the South

Johann Strauss, Jr. (1825–1899)
Austrian Composer

*Slow bow
speed*

Three-Note Slurs

Steps to Success:
- ❑ Play 3-note slurs
- ❑ Play **Three-Note Slurs** from memory
- ❑ Play pick-up note in ¾ time

183. Tricky Rhythm Time

184. Three-Note Slurs – *Memorization Line*

185. Rise Up, O Flame – *Round*

Christoph Prætorius (1535–1706)
German Composer

186. Sleeping Beauty Waltz

Peter Ilyich Tchaikovsky (1840–1893)
Russian Composer

187. Minuet

Johann Sebastian Bach (1685–1750)
German Composer

188. Forest Fawn – *Orchestra Arrangement*

Jeremy Woolstenhulme (b. 1974)
American Composer

115CO

Steps to Success:

❑ Name notes on the staff
❑ Play with good left hand shape

189. E String Easy! – *New Step for Violin and Bass*

190. Exactly E – *Duet*

191. B on E – *Steps to Learning Theory*

Write the letter name below each note.

192. Sakura

Japanese Folk Song

193. Shepherd's Hey

English Folk Song

194. Yangtze Boatman Chantey TEST LINE

Chinese Folk Song

115CO

Steps to Success:
❏ Play with good left hand shape
❏ Play with criss-cross fingering
❏ Understand *D.C. al Fine*

D.C. al Fine = go back to the beginning and play until the **Fine** (the end).

195. G Major Upper Octave Scale – *New Step for Violin*

196. Second Finger Free – *New Step for Violin & Viola*

197. Unblocked Left Hand – *New Step for Violin & Viola*

Use only 4th finger on highlighted notes.

198. Criss-Cross Applesauce – *New Step for Violin, Viola & Cello*

Anchor your 1st finger.

199. Cielito Lindo

Mexican Folk Song

200. Cripple Creek – *Orchestra Arrangement*

American Folk Song
Arr. by Jeremy Woolstenhulme (b. 1974)
Fine

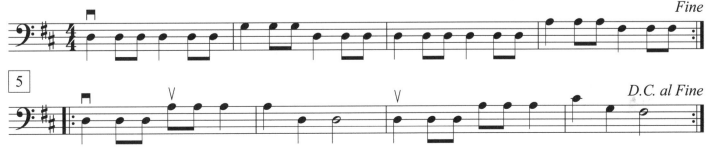

D.C. al Fine

115CO

Steps to Success:

- ❑ Play C, D, E, F on the C string
- ❑ Name notes on the staff
- ❑ Play fast-slow bow strokes in ¾ time

C String: All fingers down

201. Learning the C String – *New Step for Viola & Cello*

202. Rockin' on C – *Steps to Learning Theory*

Write the letter name below each note.

203. Volga Boatman Song

Russian Folk Song

204. Roll, Jordan, Roll – *Duet*

American Spiritual

205. The Quest

Bohemian Folk Song

"Fast Slow—"

C Major Scale

Steps to Success:
- Understand whole steps and half steps
- Play **C Major Scale** from memory
- Sight read accurately in C Major

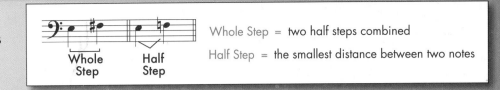

Whole Step = two half steps combined
Half Step = the smallest distance between two notes

206. C Major Scale – Memorization Line

207. We Sail the Ocean Blue from "H.M.S. Pinafore"
Sir Arthur Sullivan (1842–1900)
English Composer

208. Good Night – Round
German Folk Song

209. Blow the Man Down TEST LINE
English Sea Chantey

210. A-Tisket, A-Tasket – Sight Reading Line
American Folk Song

211. The Troupial Bird
Venezuelan Folk Song

115CO

Steps to Success:
- ❏ Play *p*, *f*, *mf* dynamics

Dynamics = softness or loudness in music	
p	= piano = soft
f	= forte = loud
mf	= mezzo forte = medium loud

212. C Major Piano

213. G Major Forte

214. D Major Mezzo Forte

215. The Little Fish

Australian Folk Song

216. Arkansas Traveler

American Folk Song

217. East Meets West: A Detective Story

Deborah Gilmour Smyth (b. 1956)
American Composer

Double Stops & Tempos

Double Stop = two notes played at the same time

Tempo = the speed of music

Moderato = medium speed   **Allegro** = fast   **Andante** = moderately slow

218. Double Stops

219. Silky Double Stops

220. Ready, Set, Place Bow

221. Double Stop March

222. Fiddle Time

223. The Old Chisholm Trail

Texan Folk Song

115CO

Steps to Success:
❏ Play with good posture and bow hold
❏ Play legato, staccato, spiccato, and accents

Legato = play smoothly and connected
Staccato = play with short, crisp bow strokes
Spiccato = play with bounced bow strokes
Accent = > = place a special emphasis on a note with the bow

224. Legato Legacy

225. Wooden Shoe Dance

Victor Herbert (1859–1924)
American Composer

Moderato

226. Sticky Staccato

227. Staccato March

Allegro

228. Accent Waltz

Andante

229. Spiccato Bounce

Allegro

230. Pogo Stick

Allegro

231. Two-Octave C Major Scale – *New Step for Viola & Cello*

232. C Major Chorale – "Wachet auf"

Philipp Nicolai (1556–1608)
German Composer

233. Two-Octave G Major Scale – *New Step for Violin*

234. G Major Chorale – "Wie schön leuchtet der Morgenstern"

Philipp Nicolai (1556–1608)
German Composer

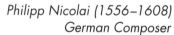

235. One-Octave D Major Scale

236. D Major Chorale – "Lobe den Herren"

Straslund Gesangbuch (1665)

Chanson Belle

Cello Solo with Piano Accompaniment

Jeremy Woolstenhulme (b. 1974)
American Composer

Piano Accompaniment

115CO

D.S. al Coda = go back to the 𝄋 sign.
When you reach the **Coda** Sign ⊕,
skip to the **Coda**.

Conquest
for String Orchestra

Jeremy Woolstenhulme (b. 1974)
American Composer

115CO

Glossary

1st & 2nd Ending *(35)*

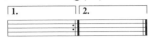

Play the 1st ending the first time through. Repeat the same music, skip the 1st ending and play the 2nd ending.

Accent *(44)*

To place a special emphasis on a note with the bow.

Arco *(14)* [Italian]
To play using the bow.

Bar Line *(4)*

A vertical line dividing the staff into measures.

Bass Clef *(4)*

Also called the F Clef. A symbol placed at the beginning of the staff used to identify the names of the lines and spaces. Cellists and bassists use bass clef.

Beat *(4)*
A steady, regular pulse in music.

Bow Lift *(16)*

Lift the bow and set it back towards the frog.

Coda *(47)* [Italian]
The final section of a piece of music.

Common Time *(12)*

The same as $\frac{4}{4}$ time.

Conducting *(36)*

Using a pattern to beat time with a hand or baton.

D.C. al Fine *(39)* [Italian]
Da Capo al Fine, go back to the beginning and play until the Fine. Do not take the repeats.

Dotted Half Note *(36)*

Receives 3 beats of sound.

Double Bar Line *(4)*

A thin and thick line marking the end of the music.

Double Stop *(43)*

Two different notes played at the same time.

Down Bow *(14)*

Pull the bow on the string away from the frog and towards the tip.

D.S. al Coda *(47)* [Italian]
Del Segno al Coda, go back to the 𝄋 sign. When you reach the Coda Sign 𝄌 skip to the Coda.

Duet *(7)*
Music with two different parts, played together.

Dynamics *(42)*
The softness and loudness in music, indicated with *f*, *mf*, *p* symbols.

Eighth Notes *(30)*

A group of two eighth notes equal one quarter note.

Fermata *(33)* [Italian]

Play the note longer than its usual value.

Fine *(39)* [Italian]
The end.

Half Note *(5)*

Receives two beats of sound.

Half Rest *(5)*

Receives two beats of silence.

Half Step *(41)*
An interval. It's the smallest distance between two notes.

Harmony *(7)*
Music that accompanies the melody. Duets, trios, and quartets feature harmony parts with the melody line.

Interval *(21)*
The distance between two notes.

Key Signature *(13, 26, 35)*

Placed at the beginning of music, it tells us which notes should be played with sharps.

Ledger Lines *(4)*

Short lines used for notes written above and below the staff.

Legato *(44)*
Play smoothly and connected.

Measure *(4)*

Also called a bar, this is the space between two bar lines. A measure is filled with a specific number of beats/counts as determined by the time signature.

Music Staff *(4)*

5 lines and 4 spaces on which musical notes are written.

Natural *(32)*

Cancels a sharp.

Octave *(21)*

The interval from one note to the next note with the same name.

Pick-Up Note *(33)*

One or more notes coming before the first full measure of music.

Pizzicato or pizz. *(4)* [Italian]
To pluck the string with the right hand index finger.

Pulse *(4)*
A steady series of beats in music.

Quarter Note *(4)*

Receives 1 beat of sound.

Quarter Rest *(4)*

Receives 1 beat of silence.

Quartet *(31)*
Music with four different parts, played together.

Repeat Sign *(6)*

Go back and play again.

Round *(21)*
Music where two or more players play the same melody but begin at different times.

Scale *(13)*
A series of notes placed in stepwise ascending or descending order.
A scale begins and ends with the note of the same letter name.

Sharp *(9)*

Raises a note ½ step.

Slur *(28)*

A curved line connecting 2 or more different pitches in a single bow stroke. Slurred notes are played smoothly.

Solo *(10)*
Music for one player.

Spiccato *(44)* [Italian]
Play with bounced bow strokes.

Staccato *(44)* [Italian]

Play with short, crisp bow strokes. Stop the bow between each note.

Tempo *(43)*
The speed of music. Tempo markings in this book are **Andante, Moderato, Allegro.**

Tie *(29)*

A curved line connecting 2 of the same pitches. Tied notes are played as 1 note.

Time Signature *(4, 12, 31, 36)*

Placed at the beginning of music, it indicates the number of beats per measure and the type of note receiving one beat.

Trio *(7)*
Music with three different parts, played together.

Tutti *(10)* [Italian]
All. Everyone plays together. It is usually marked after a solo.

Up Bow *(14)*

Push the bow on the string away from the tip and towards the frog.

Whole Note *(7)*

Receives 4 beats of sound.

Whole Rest *(7)*

Receives 4 beats of silence.

Whole Step *(41)*
An interval made up of two half steps.